NINJA BATTLES

WRITTEN BY
BETH LANDIS HESTER

CONTENTS

INTRODUCTION

A NINJA IS ALWAYS READY TO FIGHT EVIL.

The Ninja are the sworn defenders of Ninjago Island. They have been trained by the wise Master Wu to become skilled warriors. Using the ancient art of Spinjitzu and their elemental powers—fire, ice, earth, and lightning—these protectors of peace never back down from facing the forces of darkness. Who will be victorious in the battle between good and evil?

ATTACK OF THE GREAT DEVOURER!

UNLEASHED BY THE Serpentine schemer Pythor, this mighty snake is on the loose in Ninjago City, eating everything in its path and getting larger and more terrifying by the bite. To stand a chance of defeating it, the Ninja will need quick thinking and great teamwork.

DID YOU KNOW?
This monster is the same tiny snake that bit Garmadon when he was a young boy.

STRIKE ONE...
Kai, Cole, Jay, and Zane try their best Spinjitzu moves, then they blast the tune of a Serpentine-slaying flute at the snake, but they still can't defeat this super-size creature.

STRIKE TWO...
In her big Mech, Nya is able to fly in and wedge the Devourer's mouth open. It's a good idea, but the dangerous maneuver doesn't stop the Devourer, and Nya nearly ends up inside its belly.

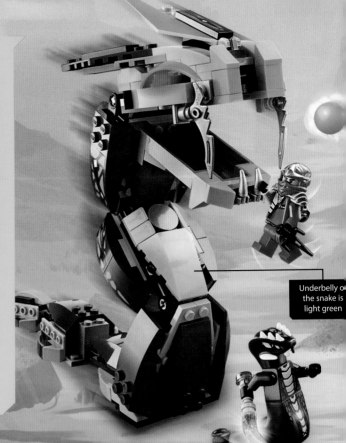

Underbelly o the snake is light green

STRIKE THREE!

The Ninja's dragons merge to form the Ultradragon—a four-headed beast with all their powers. Lloyd guides the Ultradragon toward the Great Devourer, but even a dragon can't overcome the greedy snake.

Powerful tail can sweep enemies off their feet

Red flame decoration represents Fire element

THE HUNGRY SNAKE

The Devourer eats everything in sight and grows bigger and bigger every second. It even thinks Pythor and Sensei Wu are a tasty snack! Luckily, it spits Wu and his teapot back out.

GARMADON... THE HERO?

The Devourer has a weak spot on its forehead, but the Ninja will have to trust their enemy, Garmadon, with their Golden Weapons if they hope to exploit it. With four arms, immense power, and a score to settle, he is the only one who can defeat the Devourer.

CAN YOU SURVIVE THE DARK ISLAND?

COLE KNOWS IT won't be easy to attack the Overlord's Dark Island Base —there are dangers everywhere. But if the Ninja stick together, stay hidden, and use all their skills, they should be able to defeat the Overlord and escape.

SCOUT THE ENEMY CAMP

AVOID EVIL

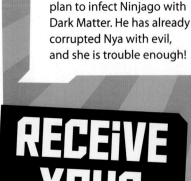

New elemental powers can be found in the Temple of Light —but you'll have to figure out on your own how to unlock them. Fortunately there seems to be some clues in the Temple, and four convenient spaces to place weapons…

The Overlord senses when enemies are near, and sends the Stone Army to imprison them. Try not to become an unwilling test subject for his plan to infect Ninjago with Dark Matter. He has already corrupted Nya with evil, and she is trouble enough!

The stone warriors speak an ancient language almost no one can understand. But by watching their movements, it's possible to see what they are up to—digging up evil Dark Matter and building the Overlord's Ultimate Weapon. Just don't get caught!

RECEIVE YOUR POWERS

BEWARE THE GARMATRON

Once the immense Garmatron is loaded up with Dark Matter, it can infect anyone with evil in a single shot. Steer clear of this dangerous machine—if you are unfortunate enough to meet it, run away as fast as you can!

RACE TO NINJAGO!

Stacked roof in the traditional Ninjago style

IF THEY ARE to have any hope of returning to Ninjago City and defeating the Overlord, the Ninja must first find the Temple of Light, unite the Elemental Swords, and activate the First Spinjitzu Master's Golden Mech. No problem!

DID YOU KNOW?
Lloyd's mother, Misako, advises the Ninja to find the Temple of Light. She has heard ancient myths detailing its power.

FAR TO GO
Lloyd's leg is injured and the Ninja have given away their elemental powers. It seems impossible the team of heroes will be able to cross the vast ocean that stands between them and Ninjago City.

Murals show Ninjago's ancient master

Weapons rack

HOME AT LAST

Revived by the Golden Ninja, the Golden Mech works like an enormous suit of armor, battle tank, and robot warrior all rolled into one. Despite his injury, Lloyd is able to fly the Mech back to Ninjago to face the Overlord. The rest of the gang follow on the Ultradragon to witness the epic showdown.

Gleaming golden armor

TEMPLE OF LIGHT

The Temple of Light looks like a peaceful palace—but as the hiding place of the Elemental Blades and Golden Mech, it holds incredible power. A few Stone Army warriors won't keep Lloyd from uncovering his destiny within its ancient walls.

THE PERFECT MATCH MACHINE

WHEN THE NINJA visit Borg Industries with the students of Wu's new academy, Nya accompanies them. Her students persuade her to try the Perfect Match Machine, which can predict your soulmate.

SURPRISE MATCH
Nya is shocked when the Perfect Match Machine suggests Cole is her ideal date, rather than Jay!

JAY AND NYA

RATiNG: COMPATIBLE

Not a perfect match, but very strong compatibility. These two cool characters bring out the best in each other.

NYA AND COLE

RATiNG: PERFECT MATCH

An ideal pairing! Common areas include strength, thoughtfulness, and temperament.

MISAKO AND WU

RATiNG: EXCELLENT

A true meeting of minds makes this an outstanding match. Obstacles stand in the way of a relationship however.

ZANE AND P.I.X.A.L.

RATiNG: COMPATIBLE

With slight modifications, a perfect match can be achieved. Programming and settings are compatible.

KAI AND SKYLOR

RATiNG: UNCERTAIN

Sparks of romance exist, but without trust the relationship cannot develop further.

SENSEI GARMADON

After he is cured of the evil that possessed him, the once-wicked Garmadon finds a new, peaceful path. At his remote monastery, Sensei Garmadon teaches the Ninja to use speed and stealth to outwit enemies—without turning to weapons or violence.

ALLY OR

IN NINJAGO, THE LINES between good and evil can sometimes get a litt blurred. Just ask these two brothers—they know that good guys and bad guys aren't always what they seem!

"THE KEY IS BALANCE."
SENSEI GARMADON

"HE'S TURNED EVIL. HELP ME!"
KAI

ENEMY?

TECH WU

Only the Digital Overlord could have retooled gentle Sensei Wu into this mean metal fighting machine! Tech Wu has all of the Sensei's skills, corrupted with a dark new mission: Help the Overlord and destroy the Ninja.

THE MIGHTY MECHDRAGON ATTACKS!

THE DIGITAL OVERLORD is determined to get his (virtual) hands on Lloyd. He believes that harnessing Lloyd's golden powers will give him the physical form he desires. The Overlord sends Tech Wu and the enormous MechDragon to track him down.

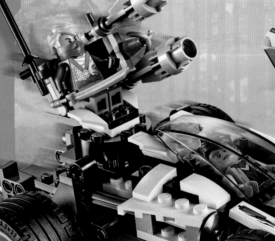

Samurai flag

PEACEFUL POP

After he becomes good again, Sensei Garmadon is eager to make up for lost time with his son. When Lloyd is forced to hide from the Digital Overlord, his father joins him for support. Garmadon tries to pass on some of his wisdom on their father-son roadtrip!

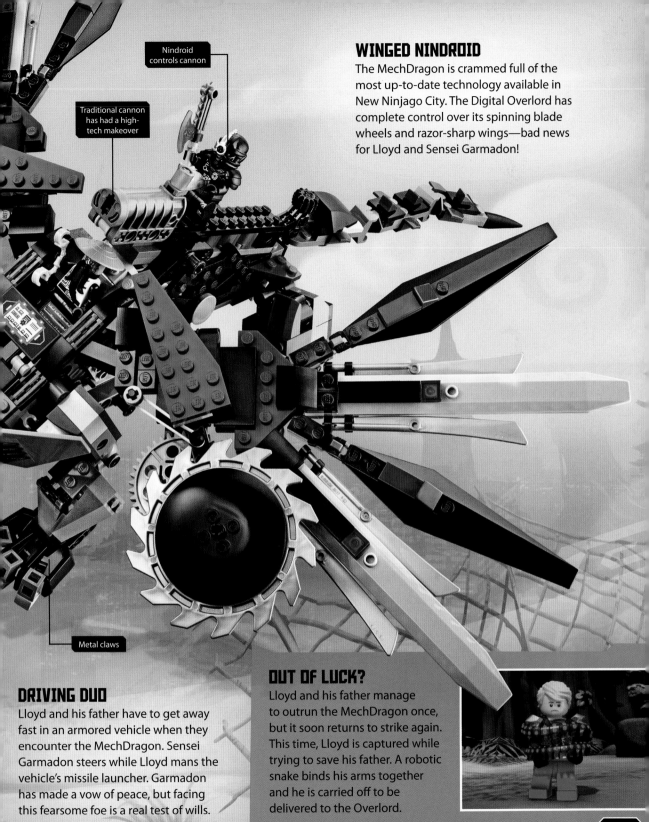

Nindroid controls cannon

Traditional cannon has had a high-tech makeover

WINGED NINDROID

The MechDragon is crammed full of the most up-to-date technology available in New Ninjago City. The Digital Overlord has complete control over its spinning blade wheels and razor-sharp wings—bad news for Lloyd and Sensei Garmadon!

Metal claws

DRIVING DUO

Lloyd and his father have to get away fast in an armored vehicle when they encounter the MechDragon. Sensei Garmadon steers while Lloyd mans the vehicle's missile launcher. Garmadon has made a vow of peace, but facing this fearsome foe is a real test of wills.

OUT OF LUCK?

Lloyd and his father manage to outrun the MechDragon once, but it soon returns to strike again. This time, Lloyd is captured while trying to save his father. A robotic snake binds his arms together and he is carried off to be delivered to the Overlord.

WHAT HAPPENS IN THE DiGIVERSE?

THANKS TO ONE of Cyrus Borg's inventions, and some technical support from P.I.X.A.L., it is possible for the Ninja to enter the digital realm where the Digital Overlord is residing. Their mission: fight and defeat the Overlord before he regains his physical form.

TECH WORLD

Inside the Digiverse, regular rules don't apply. Instead, it's as if the Ninja are characters in a video game—an idea that's thrilling to tech-fan Jay and simply terrifying to Kai. Not a gadget fan, Kai struggles to control his new powers.

IMAGINATION RULES

To cope with the ever-changing rules in the Digiverse, the Ninja must imagine the powers they need: jumping huge distances, turning upside-down, and creating vehicles out of thin air.

DID YOU KNOW?

When the Ninja wipe the Overlord from the Digiverse, Wu is no longer corrupted by evil technology. He returns to his normal self and stretches out a friendly hand to his brother.

LIGHT IN DARKNESS

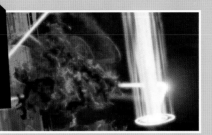

When the Digital Overlord blocks their path, the Ninja must find a way to surround him with the light of their Techno Blades. They use their minds to connect their beams and destroy the heart of the Overlord's digital system.

MEANWHILE...

While the Ninja fight in the digital world, Nya and P.I.X.A.L. take on the Nindroids in Borg Tower—struggling to protect the technology that will let the Ninja return to the real world. Wu once again battles his brother, but this time it is Sensei Garmadon protecting the Ninja!

THE ODDS OF SUCCESS ARE TOO SLIM TO CALCULATE...

THAT HAS NEVER STOPPED US BEFORE!

CAN YOU REALLY TRUST A SNAKE?

IN EVERY BEING, there is both good and evil—look at Sensei Garmadon! The slithering Serpentine have also been viewed as evil for many long years—but from their point of view, things are very different.

SHEDDING OLD SKINS

In their underground dwelling, the Serpentine have turned over a new leaf—taking lessons in good manners and educating their young about the stories they hold dear. In their way, they are trying to be unified, helpful, and good.

THE HEROES OF NINJAGO

In their legends, the Serpentine tell their children of their efforts to save the world from the evil they know is coming. When they tried to warn the humans, they were attacked and driven underground. To a loving father like Skales, being treated as evil seems a great injustice.

The Serpentine believe that a Golden Master will overturn all that is good in Ninjago, bringing about a new age of evil that cannot be defeated. Could they be mistaking the Golden Ninja for the evil Golden Master?

THE CURSE OF THE GOLDEN MASTER

DID YOU KNOW?
The Ninja believed Pythor was lost forever in the stomach of the Great Devourer. Pythor actually escaped, although the acid in the monster's belly bleached his purple scales to white.

A SNAKE AMONG SNAKES

The Ninja consult the snakes when a mysterious enemy leaves behind a white scale after a battle. They believe that the individual is working for the Digital Overlord, and is using Electrocobrai —underwater snakes that carry electricity—to power the Nindroids. The Serpentine know Pythor is the only snake capable of such mischief.

DEFEND AGAINST THE OVERLORD!

Zane's jetpack

THE WORST HAS happened—the Digital Overlord has gained a physical form and become the fabled Golden Master. He has all of Ninjago in his evil control. Can the Ninja defeat him before all hope is lost?

The Overlord's flesh form

TRAPPED NINJA

Even fighting as one, the Ninja are no match for the vast power of the Golden Master, whose golden web of power stretches across New Ninjago City.

LARGE AND IN CHARGE

After a long quest to regain a physical form, the Overlord has a physical body and more—his maniacal Mech gives him terrifying powers and abilities.

Robotic foreleg

TEMPLE OF FORTITUDE

This strong temple offers cool new armored robes for Zane, and temporary protection for t Ninja—until the Nindroids arri

ZANE'S SACRIFICE

To save his fellow Ninja, Zane sacrifices himself—plugging himself into the web and absorbing the frightful power of the Golden Master to defeat the Digital Overlord. The Ninja are devastated at the loss of their brother.

Zip wire provides a speedy descent

Stone staircase

THE TOURNAMENT OF ELEMENTS

CALLING ALL
HEROES OF NINJAGO!

Do you have what it takes to come out on top?

Find out at Master Chen's

TOURNAMENT OF ELEMENTS!

Take part in the event of the year—pitting power against power, and hero against hero, in a historic fight for glory!

WHEN: THIS WEEK
WHERE: MASTER CHEN'S ISLAND

REGISTER TODAY!

*

NINJA VS. SNAKES!

IT FEELS LIKE this has all happened before—but this new gang of snakes is a whole new threat. Master Chen is building his own Anacondrai army at a temple hidden on his secret island. He plans to start a new Serpentine War and take control of Ninjago.

Handheld sai weapon

LOOKALIKES

Pythor used to be the only one of his species, but not any more. It turns out members of the tribe all have similar traits: purple skin, red eyes, and an unnerving ability to swallow people whole.

ANACONDRAI TEMPLE

Chen takes over this ancient abandoned temple and uses is as the base for his growing snake army. It shows his admiration for the Anacondrai—this was the tribe's own temple many, many years ago

rpent head

ngs

WATCHFUL LEADER

Clutching his powerful staff, Chen oversees the battle—ready to soak up the powers of any fallen fighters.

RETURN OF THE SNAKES

Chen is obsessed with the Anacondrai and is determined to transform his army into the powerful snakes. All it takes is an ancient spell book, Clouse's magical abilities, the stolen elemental powers, and the help of Pythor!

DK

Penguin Random House

EDITORS Pamela Afram, Matt Jones,
Clare Millar, Rosie Peet
SENIOR DESIGNERS Jo Connor, David McDonald
SENIOR SLIPCASE DESIGNER Mark Penfound
EDITORIAL ASSISTANT Beth Davies
DESIGNED BY Dynamo
COVER DESIGNER Stefan Georgiou
PRE-PRODUCTION PRODUCER Kavita Varma
SENIOR PRODUCER Lloyd Robertson
MANAGING EDITOR Paula Regan
DESIGN MANAGER Guy Harvey
CREATIVE MANAGER Sarah Harland
ART DIRECTOR Lisa Lanzarini
PUBLISHER Julie Ferris
PUBLISHING DIRECTOR Simon Beecroft

Additional photography by Gary Ombler

Dorling Kindersley would like to thank:
Heike Bornhausen, Randi Sørensen,
Martin Leighton and Paul Hansford
at the LEGO Group; Radhika Banerjee, Jon Hall,
and Pamela Shiels at DK for design assistance.

First American Edition, 2016
Published in the United States by DK Publishing
345 Hudson Street, New York, New York 10014
DK, a Division of Penguin Random House LLC

www.LEGO.com/ninjago
www.dk.com

Contains content previously published in LEGO®
NINJAGO™ *Secret World of the Ninja* (2015)

001-298874-Jul/2016

A catalog record for this book is available from
the Library of Congress.

ISBN: 978-5-0010-1406-5

Printed in China

A WORLD OF IDEAS:
SEE ALL THERE IS TO KNOW